To Ben
Happy 1st Birthday

Lots of love
from

Ian, Andrea and
Jamie
xx
x .

I0830980

About this book

Many children have difficulty puzzling out letters because they are abstract symbols. Letterland's worldwide success is all about its enduring characters who give these symbols life and stop them from being abstract. In this book we meet Bouncy Ben. His story is carefully designed to emphasise the sounds that the letter 'B' makes in words. This definitive, original story book is an instant collector's classic, making learning fun for a new generation of readers.

A TEMPLAR BOOK

This edition published in the UK in 2008 by Templar Publishing
an imprint of The Templar Company plc,
The Granary, North Street, Dorking, Surrey, RH4 1DN, UK
www.templarco.co.uk

First published by Hamlyn Publishing, 1985
Devised and produced by The Templar Company plc

Copyright © 1985 by The Templar Company plc

1 3 5 7 9 8 6 4 2

All rights reserved

ISBN 978-1-84011-760-8

Printed in China

Letterland © was devised by and is the copyright of Lyn Wendon
LETTERLAND® is a registered trademark

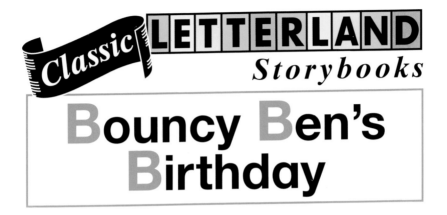

Classic LETTERLAND Storybooks

Bouncy Ben's Birthday

Written by Richard Carlisle

Illustrated by
Jane Launchbury

templar publishing

Bouncy Ben was so excited. Tomorrow was his birthday. Tucked under his blanket that night, he could hardly sleep.

He lay awake thinking of all the presents he wanted. If only he could have a new bat and ball!

He tried to imagine what other surprises might be waiting for him when he woke up.

Next morning Bouncy Ben bounded out of bed and was down to breakfast in a flash.

His brothers were already at the breakfast table munching bread and butter.

"You look bright-eyed and bushy-tailed this morning," they said. "That's because today is a special day!" said Bouncy Ben brightly.

He started to look around for his presents, but he could not see a single one. He looked underneath the table. There were none there either.

Bouncy Ben was bewildered.
He finished his breakfast and
bounced outside.
There were no presents outside,
not even under the bushes.

His brothers began playing ball near
to the bridge. Bouncy Ben hopped over
to them.

"Aren't you going to wish me Happy
B...?" Bouncy Ben started to say.
But his brothers just kept on playing.
They didn't seem to be listening.

Bouncy Ben sat by the bridge watching his brothers.
He was beginning to feel very sorry for himself. No-one seemed to have remembered his birthday!

He even sneaked another look behind some bushes to see if his presents were hidden there. But the bushes were bare.

Soon Ben's brothers had finished their game. They decided to go for a walk into the woods.

"Can I come, too?" asked Ben.
"If you really want to,"
said his brothers as they bounced along the path that led into the woods.

Bouncy Ben hopped along behind them rather slowly. Soon he was far behind. His brothers were nearly out of sight.

Bouncy Ben stopped and ate some berries. That made him feel a little better. Then he bounded ahead, expecting to see his brothers waiting for him... but they weren't.

He wasn't even sure which way they went. Ben was beginning to think he was lost.

Suddenly, he heard the sound of singing. It came from the other side of some bushes.
Ben raced towards the sounds, until he could hear the words.

He burst through the bushes.
All his brothers were there!
They had been waiting for him...
and they were singing...

"**H**appy birthday, to you.
Happy birthday, to you.
Happy birthday dear Ben,
happy birthday to you!"
they sang happily.

"You have remembered my birthday!"
shouted Ben, as he bounced into the
air with joy.

His brothers were standing by a
beautiful birthday cake with bright
blue candles. There were lots of
presents too, all neatly tied up with
big, blue ribbons.

Bouncy Ben could hardly wait to open his presents. All his brothers watched as he opened the first one. Inside was a new ball!

Then he opened the second present. Inside was a brand new bat. Just what he wanted.

Bouncy Ben beamed.

Bouncy Ben's brothers smiled too. They had another surprise for him.

"Time to play 'Blind Man's Buff'," said his brothers. They put a blindfold over his eyes and led him into a field.

"Now catch us," they cried.

Bouncy Ben tried to catch them. Instead he caught... a big, big basket!

"It's your birthday treat!"
cried his brothers, pulling off
Ben's blindfold.
"A balloon ride."
"Oh, how beautiful!" Ben shouted.
"Let's all jump into the basket."

So Bouncy Ben and his brothers all
bounced into the basket.

Up, up and away went the balloon.

Then Ben saw lots of other beautiful balloons floating up. They rose higher and higher until Ben saw that they all had letters on them. He read the words they made.

'Happy Birthday, Ben', they said.

Everyone in Letterland had remembered that today was his birthday!

"What a day!" cried Ben.
"The best birthday ever!"

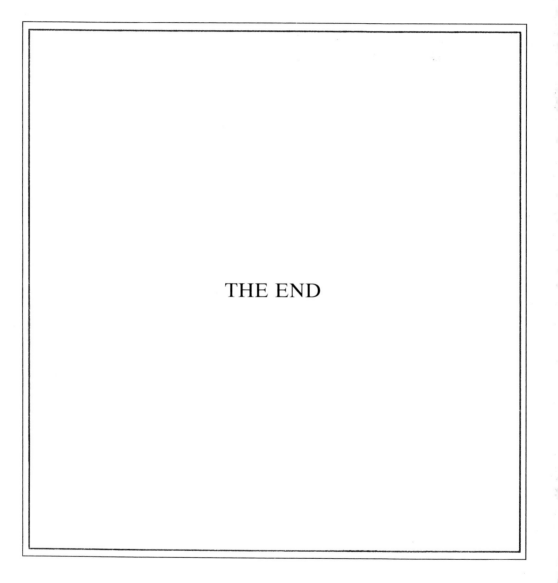

THE END